ONE HUNDRE...
in
ENGLISH USAGE
and
COMPOSITION

By

T. H. DALZELL, M.A., H.Dip. Ed.

BOOK I

© **T. H. DALZELL: 1980**

ISBN 0 7169 4015 9

A CENTURY SERIES

ROBERT GIBSON & SONS, GLASGOW, LTD.
17 FITZROY PLACE, GLASGOW G3 7SF

Genevieve Elizabeth Fletcher

PREFACE

This book, intended for the study of English by eight-year-olds in Primary and Preparatory schools, contains a variety of exercises which have proved their usefulness.

The aims of this book are:—

To supplement the teacher's own work in language training.

To help to eliminate common errors of speech and writing.

To enable the pupil to write lucid, properly-punctuated sentences.

To enlarge the pupil's vocabulary.

To provide introductory exercises in paragraphing.

To suggest suitable topics for oral and written exercises in composition.

The book should prove a valuable time-saver for the busy teacher and, in addition, allow the pupil to undertake the work for the maximum time during the English period.

The synopsis at the beginning of the book will assist the teacher to use it to the best advantage in conjunction with his own scheme of work.

T. H. D.

SYNOPSIS

SYNOPSIS *(continued)*

SENTENCE CONSTRUCTION
(continued)

To contain given words: 24.
To contain given phrases: 30.
To contain given similes: 63.
Enlarging with suitable adjs.
: 53.
From jumbled words: 10.
Making question, given answer:
51.
Re-casting, leaving out 'then' :
83.
Re-writing in plural form : 54,
84.
Re-writing using word for
phrase: 33, 91.

VERBS

Alternatives for 'went' : 92.
Are, is: 2.
Diagnostic exercise: 47, 87, 89,
Do, does: 15.
Has, have: 11.
Sounds of animals: 18, 88.
Sounds, placing in sentences :
38.
Was, were: 8.

VOCABULARY

Meaning of words, matching
exercise: 42.
Meaning of word used vari-
ously: 65.
Meaning of words from sen-
tences: 68.
Meaning from group of words :
20.
Names of young of certain
animals: 50.
Distinguishing size of objects :
39, 40.
Fitting words in 'Safety First'
sentences: 49.
Pairing words: 32.
Recognising the word not be-
longing to group: 73.
Recognising an object from
description: 59.
Synonyms: 52, 96.
Use of names in sentences
showing colour: 44.
Word-building, 'can': 77.

COMPOSITION

Exercises in Appendix.

EXERCISE 1

Some of the following can be written as sentences. Write only the sentences.

1. a white dog with black spots.
2. looking for a match
3. we have been walking for two hours
4. father shaving in the morning
5. Joan is brushing her hair
6. King George and Queen Elizabeth
7. mother knitted the scarf
8. my sister won the competition
9. away in the distance
10. John can swim

EXERCISE 2

Fill in the blanks with 'is' or 'are':

1. The egg .... in the nest.
2. The eggs .... in the nest.
3. This .... my sister.
4. .... this your puppy?
5. Some of the boys .... here.
6. There .... my overcoat.
7. .... these your books?
8. Jim, ... those your shoes?

EXERCISE 3

Re-write, putting in capital letters where they are necessary:

1. jane and jill came to my christmas party.
2. my aunt ann from america is coming to visit us in july.
3. father sailed for glasgow on thursday night.
4. next easter i hope to spend my holidays in wales.
5. the hottest of the summer months last year was august.
6. hallowe'en was on monday, 31st october this year.
7. are you going to alice's party on the third of april?
8. on august bank holiday cousin james and i went to newcastle.

EXERCISE 4

Fill in the blanks with 'a' or 'an':

1. .... apple .... day keeps the doctor away.
2. Mother gave me .... orange, ... peach and .... apricot.
3. George wore .... cap, ... scarf and .... overcoat.
4. The bird had built .... nest in .... oak tree.
5. .... uncle and .... aunt of Mary's were here for .... hour.
6. Bob had .... egg and .... rasher of bacon for breakfast.

7. We spent .... hour looking for .... neck-
lace for mother.

8. .... ox is .... very strong animal.

EXERCISE 5

Re-write the following, putting a capital letter at the
beginning of each, and a question mark at the end of those
sentences that ask questions and a full stop at the end of
those that do not ask questions:

1. give a ride on your scooter

2. have you a pen-knife

3. do you play football

4. she cannot come to-morrow

5. is your father well

6. did you enjoy your visit to Belfast

EXERCISE 6

Fill in the blanks with 'their' or 'there':

1. That is .... house over ....

2. .... are five girls in .... family.

3. .... fathers and .... mothers were ....
waiting for them.

4. In .... you will find .... clothes.

5. .... were several books on .... desk.

6. Some of .... friends went .... on a visit.

EXERCISE 7

Write out the names of:

1. 4 things you can see on your way to school.
2. 4 things kept in your kitchen.
3. 4 things used by your teacher in the classroom.
4. 4 flowers you like.
5. 4 wild animals you have heard of or read about.
6. 4 animals to be seen on the farm.

EXERCISE 8

Fill in the blanks with 'was' or 'were':

1. .... you reciting at the concert?
2. One apple .... good but several .... bad.
3. Jack and Jill .... going up the hill.
4. Joan .... small but Harry and Ernest .... tall.
5. .... your brother at school on Friday?
6. The wings of the butterfly .... beautiful.

EXERCISE 9

Use the words given in the list below to fill the spaces in the sentences:

Words: cold, bright, loud, stupid, high, sweet.

1. It was a .... morning so we wore our warm overcoats.
2. The .... explosion made me jump.

3. I am very fond of a .... orange.
4. We were tired when we reached the top of the .... hill.
5. On a .... afternoon we set off to visit granny.
6. The .... fellow had done all his work wrongly.

EXERCISE 10

Arrange the following words to make sentences:
1. world, the, round, is.
2. is, a, in, month, May, spring.
3. writing, Mary, soon, her, finish, will.
4. chair, the, under, is, dog, the.
5. growing, are, garden, tulips, the, in, the.
6. woods, in, having, picnic, were, girls, the, a, the.

EXERCISE 11

Fill in the blanks with 'has' or 'have':
1. ' Nan .... a new coat on to-day.
2. What .... she done?
3. I .... a surprise for you.
4. Willie and Hugh .... a football.
5. They .... not come to see us for a month.
6. The first of the girls .... a pretty frock.
7. You .... never heard such a story!
8. Margaret .... always been my friend.

EXERCISE 12

Write down the following pairs of words and after each pair put 'same' if they mean almost the same, or 'opposite' if they mean nearly the opposite:

Examples : old–young (opposite).
ill–sick (same).

1. old–aged.
2. early–late.
3. hot–cold.
4. below–beneath.
5. true–right.
6. great–huge.

7. replied–answered
8. more–less.
9. sly–cunning.
10. dirty–clean.
11. rich–wealthy.
12. north–south.

EXERCISE 13

Fill in the blanks with 'to', 'too' or 'two':

1. Sam had .... miles .... walk .... school.
2. The tea was .... warm .... drink.
3. Jean gave .... apples .... Dora.
4. The .... children were .... young .... come .... school.
5. The .... boys ate .... many sweets and began .... feel sick.
6. She walked .... fast and was .... tired .... play.

EXERCISE 14

Write out the names of the days of the week. Write out the names of the months of the year.

In what month does Christmas come?

On what days do we not attend school?

During what month or months do you have your longest holiday?

On what day does mother usually do her washing?

EXERCISE 15

Fill in the blanks with 'do' or 'does':

1. You .... not speak very politely.
2. She .... not always do her best.
3. .... you know your recitation?
4. They .... their homework every night after tea.
5. .... he wish to go with us?
6. Susan .... her mother's errands in the afternoons.

EXERCISE 16

Fill in the blank spaces with suitable words:

1. Mother sent me for butter, eggs and jam to the ....
2. The .... mends our footwear.
3. Father bought a new suit at the .... shop.
4. My big brother is a .... now. He is in the army.

5. Mary says she likes to look after sick people. She wants to be a ....

6. Johnny is very fond of the sea so he hopes to be a .... when he grows up.

EXERCISE 17

Fill in the blanks with 'of' or 'off':

1. I had two cups .... tea at the picnic.
2. The train ran .... the lines at the sharp bend.
3. I found the missing book but the cover was torn ....
4. Two .... them set .... through the woods.
5. On reaching the station, the train let .... steam.
6. The lower part .... the desk was broken ....

EXERCISE 18

Fill in the spaces with words telling the sounds the following make:

1. The horse ....
2. The frog ....
3. The lark ....
4. The pig .... and the dog ....
5. The rooster .... and the hens ....
6. The cat .... and the mouse ....

EXERCISE 19

Write the date for each of the following:
1. New Year's Day ....
2. Hallowe'en ....
3. Christmas ....
4. Your birthday ....
5. To-day ....
6. Boxing Day ....

EXERCISE 20

After each group of words write a word which describes all the words in the group:

Example: England, Scotland, Ireland, Wales—countries.
1. apples, oranges, grapes, plums — ....
2. potatoes, peas, beans, carrots — ....
3. horses, cows, sheep, lambs — ....
4. hens, ducks, geese, turkeys — ....
5. spiders, wasps, flies, bees — ....
6. kings, presidents, emperors, queens — ....
7. London, Dublin, Edinburgh, Paris — ....
8. beds, wardrobes, dressing-tables, chairs — ....

EXERCISE 21

Put each group of sentences in correct order so that they make a connected story:
1. (a) When the snake became well it attacked the farmer's children.

(b) At once the farmer killed it.

(c) One day a farmer found a snake, half-dead, and took it home.

2. (a) It hit on the idea of dropping pebbles into the jug until the water rose to the top.

(b) (b) A thirsty crow found a jug with water at the bottom of it.

(c) It could not reach the water with its beak.

Now give each story a title.

EXERCISE 22

Look at the apostrophe after the 'e' in "George's bat"; it shows that the bat belonged to George. The only letter that comes after the apostrophe is 's'. Use the apostrophe where it is needed in each of the following:

1. The name of Harrys dog is Rover.
2. The birds have been eating the gardeners strawberries.
3. The girls hat was lost at the playing-fields.
4. The dogs were wagging their tails happily.
5. The heavy rain destroyed the farmers crops.
6. Johns favourite game is football and Joyces is hockey.

EXERCISE 23

In the following put in the necessary capitals, full stops, question marks and apostrophes:

1. did you see joans hat.

2. mr and mrs jones are coming to aunties house for tea.
3. who broke mr greens window
4. our baby has three teeth his hair is fair
5. was jims brother alex at school on thursday or friday of last week.
6. johns new address is grove farm downpatrick co down ireland

EXERCISE 24

Make sentences containing the following groups of words:

1. cinema, Saturday, went, evening.
2. robin, winter, stays.
3. bathing, enjoy, summer, warm.
4. party, Dorothy, friends, Christmas.
5. circus, exciting, lions, act.
6. father, tools, shed, gardening.

EXERCISE 25

Fill in the blanks, using the words given in the brackets:

1. The cord would .... pass through the hole because there was a .... in it. (knot, not.)
2. I can .... the .... from my window. (sea, see.)
3. .... a trick, he managed to .... the man's car. (buy, by.)

4. Her sore .... began to .... slowly. (heel, heal.)
5. The horseman .... swiftly down the .... (road, rode.)
6. It will take you an .... to reach .... house. (our, hour.)

EXERCISE 26

Put the following sentences in their correct order to make a connected story:

1. There she stood looking at the distant sky.
2. She was watching for the sun to rise again.
3. One summer evening Nell saw the sun sink into the sea.
4. All alone she hurried down to the sandy shore.
5. The next morning she quietly stole downstairs.
6. But the sun was coming up behind her.

EXERCISE 27

From the following paragraph write down twelve words that are names:

The home of the ostrich is in the deserts of Arabia and Africa. The Arabs call it the "camel bird" from the shape of its neck and body. Like the camel, it lives in the desert and can do without water for a long time.

EXERCISE 28

Fill in the spaces with 'and' or 'but':

1. Dick fell off his bicycle .... hurt his knee.
2. Dick fell off his bicycle .... he did not hurt his knee.
3. We went to the party .... we enjoyed ourselves very much.
4. The wall is high .... I can climb it.
5. My new pen was expensive .... it does not write well.
6. The day was warm .... we thoroughly enjoyed our bathe.

EXERCISE 29

Take the following names and make two columns, putting the names which should be written with capitals in one column and the remaining names in the other:

country, town hall, holiday, november, day, christmas, india, wednesday, month, robert, building, city, person, belfast.

EXERCISE 30

Write sentences using each of the following phrases in a sentence:

1. on Saturday afternoon.
2. sheltered from the breeze
3. in the shop windows
4. rustling through the trees
5. at the Bus Stop
6. during the evening

EXERCISE 31

From the following list, write down the pairs of words that rhyme:

Luck, Jill, hearts, crown, sheep, hill, honey, sing, tarts, slow, peep, fly, knife, duck, go, king, money, eye, wife, down.

EXERCISE 32

From the following, put in pairs, the words that usually go together:

Example : father—mother

Son, boy, duke, father, daughter, duchess, mother, uncle, girl, husband, niece, king, aunt, queen, wife nephew.

EXERCISE 33

Re-write the following sentences, putting in one of the words in the given list in place of the words in italics:

Words : protect, succeed, unusual, decided, fearless, proceed.

1. It was *very strange* to see ladies boxing.
2. She did not *manage to do it.*
3. John *made up his mind* to climb.
4. The man could not *go on his way* for his horse was lame.
5. The mother bird tried to *save from harm* her young.
6. The soldier was *without fear.*

EXERCISE 34

Each of the following names means one thing: write the names meaning more than one opposite the given words:

Example : wolf—wolves.

Lady, shelf, man, wasp, child, mouse, tooth, ox, church, sheep.

EXERCISE 35

Here are six describing words which can be used to fill the spaces in the following phrases:

Describing words : calm, high, moving, clear, distant, brown.

1.	a .... rock.	4.	a .... steamer.
2.	some .... seaweed.	5.	the .... sea.
3.	the ...:........ pool.	6.	the .... waves.

When you have completed the phrases, make sentences using each phrase in a sentence.

EXERCISE 36

Choose the words in column (B) which complete the sentences commenced by the words in column (A):

	(A)	(B)
1.	Clouds are floating	in the basket.
2.	Poppies peep	in the fountain.
3.	Oranges are	among the barley.
4.	Water splashes	in the meadow.
5.	Grass grows	in the sky.

Re-write your sentences, commencing with the words you found in column (B).

EXERCISE 37

Fill in each space with the proper word:

1. Cows sleep in a ....
2. Horses sleep in a ....
3. Pigs sleep in a ....
4. Pigeons sleep in a ....
5. Nestlings sleep in a ....
6. Dogs sleep in a ....
7. Pet rabbits sleep in a ....
8. Bees sleep in a ....

EXERCISE 38

From the given list of 'sound' words, fill the spaces in the following sentences:

Words: creaking, croaking, rustling, purring, humming, ticking, singing, chirping, rumbling, whistling.

1. The clock was .... loudly.
2. We could hear thunder .... in the distance.
3. The cat was .... contentedly by the fire.
4. The pupils were .... a merry song.
5. The old door was .... on its hinges.
6. The leaves were .... in the evening breeze.
7. In the garden bees were .... and birds were ....
8. By the pond frogs were ....
9. The wind was .... in the chimney.

EXERCISE 39

(A) **Which is the larger of the following?**

1. tea-spoon—tablespoon.
2. road—lane.
3. boy—policeman.
4. orange—marble
5. gooseberry—plum.

(B) **Which is the smaller of the following?**

1. palace—house.
2. shrub—tree.
3. city—town.
4. foal—horse.
5. giant—dwarf.

EXERCISE 40

Fill in the second word in each of the following pairs:

1. cups and ....
2. ducks and ....
3. knives and ....
4. cocks and ....
5. salt and ....
6. lords and ....
7. brothers and ....
8. shillings and ....
9. women and ....
10. pens and ....

EXERCISE 41

Fill in the blanks with the correct words taken from the given list:

Words : *rake, thermometer, trowel, saw, sewing machine, tractor.*

1. A carpenter uses a ......
2. A bricklayer uses a ......
3. A dressmaker uses a ......
4. A nurse uses a ......
5. A gardener uses a ......
6. A farmer uses a ......

EXERCISE 42

Here are the names of different things:

frog, cow, bus, bicycle, star, ice, rose, candle, fire, door-bell.

Write the name of the thing which:

1. Carries passengers.
2. Is cold.
3. Gives off heat.
4. Can leap.
5. Has two wheels.
6. Has a sweet perfume.
7. You ring.
8. Gives milk.
9. Shines at night.
10. Can show light.

EXERCISE 43

Here are the names of different shop-keepers:

butcher, baker, grocer, draper, fishmonger, green-grocer, confectioner, news-agent, chemist, ironmonger.

Write the name of the shop-keeper who can sell us:

1. Coats.
2. Sweets.
3. Pills.
4. Meat.
5. Cheese
6. Nails.
7. Daily papers.
8. Vegetables
9. Loaves.
10. Herrings.

EXERCISE 44

Write a sentence about each of the following things telling of its colour:

1. Banana.
2. Pillar-box.
3. Snow.
4. Tinned salmon.
5. Tar.
6. Chocolate.
7. Grass.

EXERCISE 45

Each of the words in the following groups means one thing: re-write the words to mean more than one thing. There is a difference in the way you do each group.

1. boy, pen, book.
2. lady, baby, daisy.
3. knife, wife, life.
4. church, brush, fox.
5. tooth, goose, foot.

EXERCISE 46

There are mistakes in the sentences below. Re-write them correctly.

1. We go to church on sundays.
2. Where does harry live.
3. john and i were in londonderry at the week-end.
4. when he saw us the blind man smiled
5. mollys brother ernest won first prize.
6. miss brown told us to take out our english books.
7. the ice-cream made us feel warm and comfortable.

EXERCISE 47

Here are some doing-words:

lapped, nibbled, crunched, gulped, sipped, cropped, swallowed.

Fill in the spaces in the following:

1. The boy .... his toast.
2. The cat .... milk from the saucer.

3. The mouse .... the cheese.
4. The horse .... the grass.
5. The lady .... her tea slowly.
6. The boy .... the nasty medicine.
7. The hungry animal .... the meat in lumps.

EXERCISE 48

Give the opposite of each word in italics:

1. a *hot* meal.
2. a *heavy* load.
3. a *dull* morning.
4. a *clever* pupil.
5. a *kind* man.
6. a *young* lady.
7. a *cruel* boy.
8. a *short* journey.
9. a *tame* animal.
10. a *cross* pupil.

EXERCISE 49

It is very important to practise 'Safety First.' Fill in the blanks in the following sentences with words taken from the given list:

Words : play, straight, both, road crossing, hang, look.

1. Always .... both ways before crossing the street.
2. Don't .... on to a moving lorry.
3. Never .... on a busy street.
4. Use .... hands to steer your bicycle.
5. Walk .... across the road if you have to cross.
6. In the city cross only at the proper ....

EXERCISE 50

What do you call the <u>young</u> of each of the following:

1. A cat.
2. A dog.
3. A hen.
4. A duck.
5. A cow.

6. A sheep.
7. A horse.
8. A wolf.
9. A blackbird.
10. A pig.

EXERCISE 51

Write the questions to which the following are the answers:

1. I am eight years old.
2. I live at 48 Main Street.
3. I am in Miss Black's class.
4. I like drawing best.
5. I have dinner in the school canteen.
6. Our school day ends at a quarter past three.

EXERCISE 52

In each of the following lines, which of the words in small letters, has <u>the same or nearly the same</u> meaning as the word in capital letters at the beginning of the line?

1. BRIGHT—shining, light, polish.
2. WICKED—good, giant, evil.
3. SOFTLY—simply, quietly, easily.
4. PLEASANT—great, thankful, cheerful.

5.   HANDSOME—prince, good-looking, tall.
6.   CROOKED—straight, robber, bent.
7.   SHARP—needle, pointed, edge.
8.   TALL—high, building, size.
9.   PALE—bucket, moon, white.
10. HEALTHY—wealthy, sound, powerful.

EXERCISE 53

Re-write the following sentences, adding describing words to tell about the names in italics:

1.   The *girl* ate the *pudding*.
2.   The *donkey* was pulling the *cart*.
3.   The *fireman* climbed the *ladder*.
4.   The *lady* gave me the *orange*.
5.   The *man* saved the *child*.
6.   The *artist* painted the *picture*.

EXERCISE 54

Re-write the following sentences, telling about more than one person in each:

1.   The lady was looking at the shop-window.
2.   A merry child is like a ray of sunshine.
3.   The man was a champion boxer.
4.   Her cousin is working in an office.
5.   His brother is a doctor.
6.   My uncle lives in America.

EXERCISE 55

Add words to make the following complete sentences :
1. I like apples because ....
2. I eat them when ....
3. I buy them sometimes, if ....
4. When .... John went home.
5. She found her hat where ....
6. The man had to run because ....
7. Because .... he was out of breath when ....

EXERCISE 56

Fill in the correct word in the spaces:
1. Mother went to buy some .... (meet, meat).
2. I will .... you at the shop. (meat, meet.)
3. Jill is .... after her illness. (week, weak.)
4. There are seven days in a .... (week, weak).
5. The fire in the .... was burning low. (great, grate.)
6. .... crowds of people came to the Show. (great, grate.)

EXERCISE 57

Re-write each of the following sentences in another way, without changing the meaning:

Example : As soon as the bell rang, the girls hurried to school

The girls hurried to school as soon as the bell rang.

1. The poor blind man stood by the cinema door.
2. She was waiting patiently to cross the street.
3. The boy slipped quietly and carefully out of the front door.
4. I drew teacher's attention by raising my hand.
5. When the policeman appeared, the boys disappeared like magic.
6. Because it was cold, we wore our winter coats.

EXERCISE 58

Write out the following words, and after each put the name of the shop at which you could buy the things:

1. Chocolate.
2. Hats.
3. Screws.
4. Sausages.
5. Jam.
6. Haddock.
7. Breakfast rolls.
8. Magazines.
9. Medicine.
10. Cabbages.

EXERCISE 59

Read the following and try to find out what is described in each:

1. I am long and thin, and my outside is made of wood. Down the centre of me is a black substance. Before I can be used, my wooden outside must be partly cut away. There are certain to be a great many like me used in your school.

2. You may sit on my saddle. Your legs will move us along, but you will not walk. We shall move quickly, and you must steer. I need cleaning and oiling.

3. I have a body something like a box without a lid. I have two legs, two handles and a wheel. Sometimes I am made of wood, sometimes of iron.

EXERCISE 60

Fill in the spaces with the given phrases:

Phrases : like a child; like a needle; like a wheel; like glass; like a bird.

1. The little bone had a sharp point ....
2. The lady sang ....
3. The top of the frozen pond was ....
4. The old lady cried ....
5. The flower-bed was shaped ....

EXERCISE 61

From the given list of articles which do we use:

1. To dress our hair?
2. To stir the fire?
3. To close out the light?
4. To sew on a patch?
5. To tie up a parcel?
6. To cut bread or cake?
7. To keep our door from opening?

8.   To put wall-paper on a room?
9.   To hold the floor-boards in place?
10. To fasten on our shoes?
11. To chop wood?
12. To cut cloth?

Articles : lock, thread, axe, scissors, paste, comb, poker, string, knife, laces, nail, blind.

EXERCISE 62

Use the given groups of words to complete the sentences commenced below:

Groups of words : has long ears; is used for writing; lives in Holland; hide the sun; had glass slippers; gather honey; are sour.

1. A Dutchman ....
2. Clouds ....
3. Lemons ....
4. Ink ....

5. Bees ....
6. Cinderella ....
7. A rabbit ....

EXERCISE 63

Make sentences using the groups of words below, telling how something was done.

Example: like a hare. The frightened boy ran like a hare.

1. like a mouse.
2. like a lion.
3. like a crow.

4. like a man.
5. like a donkey.

EXERCISE 64

From the list of given words, choose a suitable one to fill each of the spaces in the phrases below:

Words : tiny, huge, painful, difficult, sharp, sweet, fast, black, red, white.

1. a .... needle.
2. a .... rose.
3. a .... wound.
4. a .... train.
5. a .... task.

Now use each completed phrase in a sentence.

EXERCISE 65

Read the following sentences, then answer the questions below:

1. The gentleman wore a *top-hat.*
2. Mary was speaking *at the top of her voice.*
3. Tom ran *at top speed.*
4. I looked him over *from top to toe.*
5. John put on his *top-coat.*

(a) Tell in different words, what kind of hat the gentleman wore.
(b) Was Mary whispering, talking quietly or shouting?
(c) How did Tom run?
(d) What does "top" mean in the fourth sentence?
(e) Give another name for the kind of coat John wore.

EXERCISE 66

Fill in the blank spaces with a word <u>opposite</u> in meaning to that in italics:

1. They travelled *night* and ...., from *sunrise* to ....
2. The wind blew *hot* and then ....
3. From *far* and .... the people came.
4. A tiger is *wild* but our cat is ....
5. In turn, the road was *up-hill* and .... all the way.

EXERCISE 67

A hundred years ago people travelled by coach. Name <u>five</u> ways by which we can travel now.

From this list, write down <u>five</u> words that should have capital letters:

lad, ireland, street, dublin, teacher, lucy, town, brother, road, paul, land, february.

Write the names of:

two blue things; two yellow things; two red things; two green things; two white things.

EXERCISE 68

Read these sentences:

1. Harry went home as fast as he could.
2. After walking a mile, William went back.

3.   Into the water leapt Hugh head first.
4.   Andrew remained sitting for a while.
5.   Tom was seen no more.

Now say which boy:

disappeared?   dived?   hurried?
returned?   rested?

EXERCISE 69

Look at the list of words following:

Curved, straight, circular, blunt, flat, oval, sharp, hollow.

Which of the words above describe these:

pancake? bow? spear? finger-point? wall of a room? tree trunk in which you can hide?

EXERCISE 70

(a) **Write down <u>five</u> words which we might use to describe the sky at different times of the year.**

(b) **Here are five names:**

lamb, snail, pig, dunce, fox.

Choose the best word from this list to go with each of the names above:

slow, cunning, playful, fat, stupid.

EXERCISE 71

Fill in the blank spaces with suitable describing words:

1. We shouted with joy at the .... news.
2. The soldier received a medal for his .... act.
3. The lady staggered along carrying a .... bag.
4. It was difficult to walk for there had been a .... fall of snow.
5. He felt cold for his coat was ....

EXERCISE 72

In what place do you usually see:

1. Bathers?
2. A minister preaching?
3. Buses?
4. Postage stamps for sale?
5. Mickey Mouse?
6. A nurse?
7. A motor-mechanic?
8. A page boy or 'boots'?

EXERCISE 73

In the groups of words below, the word in capital letters at the left of each line includes all the others but one. Write down the word that does not belong to each group.

1. FOOD — porridge, meat, vegetables, saucers, cake.
2. FURNITURE — chair, table, kitchen, sideboard, bookcase.

3. NOISES–bang, clang, crash, machine, squeak.
4. BUILDINGS — street, church, cinema, house, palace.
5. COINS — penny, dollar, franc, lira, cheque.
6. FLOWERS — roses, pansies, grass, daffodils, snowdrops.

EXERCISE 74

Make sentences by taking first, words from "A", then from "B" and then from "C":

	A	B	C
1.	The bees	do not come	in the trees
2.	Frost and snow	are flying	in the east
3.	The birds	rises	at night
4.	The sun	are singing	from flower to flower
5.	The moon	shines	in summer

EXERCISE 75

In the following sentences, fill in capital letters, full-stops, question marks and apostrophes:
1. Is that your sister Marys coat
2. my dogs name is rover he likes to go for the newspaper.
3. was that toms book on the desk
4. have you seen my pencil it is a red one
5. i am going to newcastle would you like to come
6. my brother william is a soldier he is going to china soon

EXERCISE 76

Arrange the following groups of sentences in their proper order:

1. He is eleven years old.
   Saturday last was his birthday.
   My brother's name is William.
2. It was quite late when they arrived home.
   The children were at a social.
   They enjoyed themselves very much.
3. They found a robin's nest.
   It was in an old piece of piping.
   The boys were playing hide-and-seek in the park.
   There were three eggs in it.
4. It was a beautiful summer day.
   We went to visit auntie in the country.
   Then we felt cool.
   We had a bathe in the river.

EXERCISE 77

From the information given below, make words beginning with 'can':

1. Something which can show light—............
2. A singing bird kept in some homes—............
3. A kind of cloth used to make sails and tents—..........
4. A heavy gun—............
5. A boat made from a hollowed tree-trunk—............
6. A place where school meals are served—............
7. Something which most of us like to eat—............
8. Something we do not like even if we are naughty
   —............

EXERCISE 78

From the brackets, choose a word with the opposite meaning to that at the beginning of the line:

1. WRONG—(best, bad, right, good).
2. DAY—(morning, night, noon, evening).
3. STRONG—(weak, hard, large, small).
4. SLOW—(hurry, run, quickly, fast).
5. HOT—(cool, cold, freezing, burning).
6. SHORT—(high, long, large, strong).
7. WEAK—(hard, strong, big, rough).

EXERCISE 79

Fill the blank spaces, using the words given in the list below.

Words : merrily, easily, sweetly, correctly, carefully, quietly.

1. Margaret sang .... at the party.
2. I lifted the injured bird ....
3. The clever girl always did her sums ....
4. As granny was very ill, we spoke ....
5. We laughed .... at the clown.
6. I can do that very ....

EXERCISE 80

Fill the blanks with words made from those in italics :

1. This is a *slow* bus. The bus runs ....
2. The man made a *quick* jump. The man jumped ....

3. He received a *bad* burn. He was .... burned.
4. The *bright* light shines. The light shines ....
5. This question is *easy* to do. This question is .... done.

EXERCISE 81

Re-write the following sentences, changing the position of the phrase in italics.

Example: From the neighbouring school came the boys.
The boys came from the neighbouring school.

1. A little cottage stood *near the shore.*
2. A steep hill was *on their right.*
3. The oaks and firs stood *around me.*
4. The old mill wheel makes music *from dawn to dark.*
5. The bell rang *sadly.*
6. The wheels went *round.*

EXERCISE 82

Join each pair of sentences below, using these joining words:

or, because, if, but, so.

1. He was tired. He sat down.
2. She bought the bread. She was hungry.
3. You can have milk. You can have tea.
4. The fairies run. You go near.
5. The coat is good. It is too short.

EXERCISE 83

Tell this story over again, but use 'then' not more than once:

The spider made a big web in the garden. Then she sat in a corner and watched. Then down flew a little fly into that web. Then the fly could not get out. Then the spider had a good dinner and hoped for more.

EXERCISE 84

Change the name words in the following sentences to mean more than one, and make other changes that are necessary.

Example: My foot was hurt. My feet were hurt.

1. The boat has oars.
2. The book is torn.
3. The woman screams.
4. The pen scratches.
5. Does the girl know how to sing?

EXERCISE 85

Fit each of the describing words below to one of the name words:

Describing words : sunny, rosy, beautiful, hungry, rough, sharp.

Name words : children, needle, sky, garden, waves, apples.

Now use each of the completed phrases in a sentence.

EXERCISE 86

Write down the following words and beside each put its opposite:

Loose, brave, honest, tidy, careful, cruel, safe, straight, blunt, long, true, strong, soft, lazy, idle, polite.

EXERCISE 87

Use each of the following 'action' words in sentences:

roar, hum, chatter, crows, bleats, nibble, growls, chews.

EXERCISE 88

Write down the sound words for each of the following:

Example : The frog croaks.

Cat, dog, hen, sparrow, donkey, snake, owl, dove, grasshopper, elephant.

EXERCISE 89

Fill in the blanks with the correct form of the 'action' word in brackets:

1. He .... the work last week. (do)
2. I .... Tom a few days ago. (see)
3. He .... off when he saw me. (run)
4. The wind .... hard last night. (blow)
5. She .... to cry when she saw me. (begin)
6. Uncle .... me a book yesterday. (give)
7. I have .... my new doll. (break)
8. The boy has .... down the stairs. (fall)

EXERCISE 90

In the following sentences, put words that tell <u>when</u> something is done:

Words: soon, now, immediately, late, often, sometimes.

1. Father is coming ....
2. Your brother is working ....
3. Children .... play in our garden.

In the following sentences, put words that tell <u>where</u> something is done:

Words: here, there.

4. My old master lives ....
5. The miners went .... to their work.

In the following sentences, put words that tell <u>how</u> something is done:

Words: softly, slowly, neatly, sadly.

6. We climbed the steep hill ....
7. Children should work .... in their books.
8. The little girl spoke very ....

EXERCISE 91

Re-write the following sentences, putting in one word from the given list in place of the words in italics:

Words: repeat, contained, suddenly, escape, entrance, arrive, returned, several.

1. We found the *way in* to the park.
2. When we *came back* we had dinner.
3. Will she *get there* soon?

4.   He gave me *four or five* apples.
5.   *All at once* the ice broke.
6.   The prisoner tried to *get away*.
7.   They asked him to *say again* his name.
8.   The basket *had* eggs *in it*.

EXERCISE 92

The word 'went' is often overworked. Re-write the following sentences, putting in more suitable words taken from the given list, in place of the words in italics:

Words: hurried, entered, struggled, climbed, continued, crawled.

1.   The man *went up* the mountain.
2.   The boy *went on* against the wind.
3.   The train *went into* the station.
4.   The snail *went* down the leaf.
5.   The fire *went on* burning.
6.   The girl *went quickly* to the station.

EXERCISE 93

Write out this story, putting in the missing words:

A dog had stolen a .... of meat out of a .... shop, and was crossing a stream, when he .... himself in the .... Thinking that it was .... dog with .... of meat, he made up his .... to get that too, but in snapping at the .... he .... the meat he was carrying, and so .... all.

EXERCISE 94

Write out this story, putting in the missing words and full stops:

1. He .... his horse and away it .... he soon .... home and there he found his brothers one brother had a big brown horse and the other had a .... one when the old man saw the horses he said that the white horse could run with great ....

Do this story in the same way as that above:

2. Red Riding Hood took the basket and started on her .... through the wood to her grand-mother's .... on the way she .... a wolf .... asked her where she was going when he had .... all about her grandmother he left her .... she went her way singing gaily.

EXERCISE 95

Re-write the following sentences properly:

1. jack brown and mary have gone to london
2. mrs murphy gave sally a doll on her birthday
3. i shall call my elf robin goodfellow
4. mrs williams calls her son ted and her daughter lily
5. mr johnston gave harry a book called alice in wonderland.
6. will joyce come with me to blackpool next july.

EXERCISE 96

Re-write the following sentences, putting in words of the same meaning in place of those in italics:
1. The king had a *hasty* temper.
2. I shall never be so *foolish.*
3. She *fell* into a heavy sleep.
4. He *bawled* in a great rage.
5. His wife replied *quietly.*
6. You are my parting *gift,* and the treasure that I *value* most.

In the following, choose a word from the brackets which has the same meaning as that in capital letters at the beginning:
1. OLD—(elderly, fifty, grey-haired).
2. FLOCK—(several, drove, sheep).
3. SKIN—(orange, thick, peel).
4. SMELL—(delicious, scent, roses).
5. GUIDE—(lead, follow, safety).
6. WORK—(hard, wages, toil).

EXERCISE 97

Re-write the following sentences correctly:
1. There were a boy on the road.
2. My pencil is broke.
3. Them boys is always shouting at me.
4. Me and our Fred gathered nuts.
5. This learned me a lesson.
6. Us three will carry the box.
7. Kate and Jack is good children.
8. Tom hurted hisself bad.

EXERCISE 98

Fill in the blank spaces with rhyming words:
1. "Birdie, rest a little longer.
   Till your little ...."
2. "Little Master Mouse
   You'd better leave ...."
3. "The bee is a rover.
   He feeds on ...."
4. "If you wear a woven ring,
   You can hear ...."

EXERCISE 99

From the group of describing words, choose one word to go with each of the 'name' words:

Describing words: great, creamy, strong, loose, pretty, empty.

Name words: man, maiden, forest, jug, milk, threads.

Now use each pair of words in a sentence.

EXERCISE 100

Fill in the capital letters and punctuation marks in the following:
1. the boy next door has three sisters may mary and gertie.
2. i hope i shall win a prize at the easter term examination.
3. did you see mr young last friday
4. my sister ann is going to new zealand next september

5. billy and i play football every saturday in the park
6. how did alex manage to reach glasgow on sunday
7. susan green and john davis were the best pupils in their class at the christmas examinations
8. when did betty take margaret to flowerdale market

SUBJECTS FOR COMPOSITION EXERCISES

1. Myself.
2. My pet.
3. My granny's cat.
4. A boy or girl in your class.
5. An uncle or aunt.
6. Apples
7. The clock.
8. My school-bag.
9. My family.
10. My bedroom

11. Our school.
12. Our classroom.
13. Our kitchen.
14. My winter coat.
15. My doll (Or my gun).
16. A sweet shop.
17. The postman.
18. The policeman.
19. Preparing for Christmas
20. The journey to school.

21. At the breakfast table.
22. A day at the sea-side.
23. A journey by bus or train.
24. In our garden.
25. Making a cup of tea.
26. Setting the table for tea.
27. Lighting a fire.
28. Washing my hands.
29. Cleaning my shoes.
30. Making a toy-cart (or a doll's frock).
31. Robin Redbreast tells his story.

32. "I am a little mouse." Complete this story.

33. "I am a little fairy." Complete this story.

34. Boys–boat–lake. Write an adventure story.

35. Snowstorm–mother's warning–way to school–snowballing–broken window–complaint.

36. A little boy and girl playing near the fire–the girl's frock catches fire.

37. A birthday party.

38. My Christmas stocking.

39. Mother Hubbard tells her story.

40. A day in the life of the old woman who lives in the shoe.

41. Cinderella at the Ball

42. My good turn.

43. At the market.

44. Safety First.

45. At the circus.

46. The Post Office.

47. A wet Saturday.

48. A house I like to visit.

49. Chased by a dog.

50. My chum.

51. A picnic.

52. Miss Muffet tells her story.

53 Suppose you are in an aeroplane. Describe the countryside in a flight over your home.

54. Suppose you are a policeman. Tell how you found a little child that was lost.

55. Christmas Day.

56. Buying a present for mother's birthday (or father's birthday).

57. A summer evening.

58. A game I like.

59. When I met Santa Claus.

60. A kind lady I know.

48

61. My favourite toy.
62. Play-time in school.
63. A pound to spend.
64. The ice-cream man.
65. When I'm grown up.
66. What I like to do best in school.
67. A race I won.
68. One night I had a dream.
69. If I were mother. (If I were father).
70. That was the happiest day in my life.
71. My bath.
72. My lunch.
73. Going to bed . . . rising.
74. Making toffee.
75. Making jam.
76. The sun.
77. A soldier.
78. Clothes.
79. The first thing I remember.
80. A purse.
81. The rainbow.
82. A holiday place I know well.
83. The meal I like best.
84. The bees.
85. The people who live in snow-houses.
86. The birds in spring.
87. Saving my pence.
88. An orange.
89. Houses.
90. I was very sorry because it happened.

Printed by Russell Print., Blantyre